YO DEATH

BOYHOOD OF A SUPERFIEND

MANDARIN

intro

JUDGE DEATH is the greatest foe and arch-enemy of future lawman Judge Dredd. As Moriarty was to Sherlock Holmes, so is Judge Death to Dredd. He has a simple philosophy – ALL LIFE IS A CRIME! Only the dead are truly innocent, according to Death's twisted logic, so it is his duty to give everyone the innocence they need. Since his first appearance more than ten years ago, the alien superfiend from another dimension has returned again and again to bring death to Dredd's world.

During the dark days of NECROPOLIS, Death and his fellow Dark Judges (Fear, Fire and Mortis), seized control of Mega-City One and killed more than 60 million citizens before being beaten by Judge Dredd. Just the mention of Judge Death's name strikes terror into the heart of Mega-City's population.

YOUNG DEATH is the story of his lifetime, as told to Mega-City journalist Brian Skuter in the days after Necropolis. Discover the secrets of this superfiend, how he killed his dog, his family, his entire planet and how he became the deadliest of Dredd's foes!

RIGHT THIS WAY— **OW!** OH DEAR!

Bonk!

I'M SURE IT WAS—

DEAR ME—

AHH! HERE WE ARE!

RIGHT THIS WAY, MR SKUTER.

IT SEEMED A PERFECTLY NORMAL HABHOLD, NO HINT THAT ANYTHING MIGHT BE AMISS.

THE LANDLADY WAS A TRIFLE SHORTSIGHTED ADMITTEDLY— BUT SURELY IT WAS INCONCEIVABLE THAT SHE COULD FAIL TO NOTICE THE PRESENCE OF A MALEVOLENT ALIEN BEING WITHIN HER WALLS.

THIS IS IT, I THINK!

Rap! Rap!

AND YET...

CREEEEEEEEE

MR De'ATH— IT'S YOUR VISITOR.

I'LL LEAVE YOU. CUP OF SYNTHI-CAF PERHAPS?

NO...NO THANKS.

AND YET, AS THE COLD BLAST FROM THE ROOM HIT ME, I KNEW...

ER, HI. I'M BRIAN SKUTER.

Bonk!

OH DEAR!

COME CLOSSSER. DON'T BE AFFFRAID. I WON'T HURT YOU. I HAVVVE GROWN SSSICK OF KILLINGGG. THESSE DAYSSSS...I WOULDN'T HURT A FLY.

"PSYCHO", RIGHT?

SSSOME MIGHT SSSAAY THAT, MR SSSKUTER.

NO, I MEAN, THE OLD 2-D FLIK. THAT'S LIKE WHAT NORMAN BATES SAID, IN "PSYCHO". YOU A HITCHCOCK FAN?

HITCHHHCOCK... ISSS THAT A DISSSEASSSE?

NO, HE'S A— OH! I SEE!

HA HA. VERY DROLL.

SO, YOU'VE GOT A STORY TO TELL--

SILLY ME! HA HA! OF COURSE YOU DO!

I'LL BE TAKING NOTES, BUT I'D LIKE TO RECORD THIS INTERVIEW AS WELL, SO IF YOU DON'T MIND, FIRST WE'LL DO A SOUND CHECK.

COULD YOU... HISS INTO THIS?

I HAVVVE CUT YOU A LOT OF SSSLACK ALREADY, MR SSSKUTER. I WARN YOU, DO NOT ABUSSSSE MY TOLERANCCCE.

FINE! COMING THROUGH LOUD AND PROUD!

THIS IS BRIAN SKUTER. I'M IN APARTMENT 133b SYLVIA PLATH BLOCK—

NO ADDRESSSSESS! MY WHEREABOUTSSS MUSSST REMAIN A SSSECRET!

HA HA. OF COURSE. SILLY.

THIS IS BRIAN SKUTER. I'M AT A SECRET LOCATION SOMEWHERE IN MEGA-CITY ONE, WHERE I'M ABOUT TO INTERVIEW JUDGE DEATH.

JUDGE DEATH— CHIEF CHEEZ OF THE DARK JUDGES, THOSE SINISTER BEINGS FROM ANOTHER DIMENSION WHERE LIFE ITSELF IS A CRIME— YOU CAME CLOSE TO DESTROYING THE CITY DURING NECROPOLIS. DESPITE AN INTENSIVE MANHUNT YOU'VE BEEN MISSING EVER SINCE—

OBVIOUS QUESTION—WHAT HAPPENED?

I DID NOT BRINGGG YOU HERE TO EXPLAIN MY MOVEMENTSS, MR SSSKUTER. HOWEVVER, I WILL INDULGGE YOU JUSSST ONCCCE...

WHEN THE END CAME IT WASSS A SSSIMPLE MATTER TO LOSSSE MYSELF AMONG THE RANKSSS OF THE JUDGGGED. THERE WERE SSSO MANY...

SSSO MANYYYY...

AS HE SPOKE I NOTICED A CERTAIN SADNESS IN HIS VOICE, AS IF THE PAIN OF DEFEAT HAD NOT LEFT HIM UNSCARRED. DID JUDGE DEATH, KILLER OF MILLIONS, HAVE A HUMAN SIDE?

PIT 12

HERE LIE MILLIONS WHO PERISHED DURING THE DARK DAYS OF NECROPOLIS MAY THEY FIND ETERNAL PEACE

THIS IS SICK!

HERE LIE MILLIONS WHO PERISHED DURING THE DARK DAYS OF NECROPOLIS MAY THEY FIND ETERNAL PEACE
BY ORDER JUSTICE DEPT

GRUD! THE STENCH—!

THAT'S THE SMELL OF MONEY, PAL!

AFTER THE BIG NEC THERE WAS SO MANY BODIES THEY DIDN'T BOTHER TO SEARCH 'EM OR NOTHIN'— JUST SCOOPED 'EM UP AN' DUMPED 'EM ALL IN THE CURSED EARTH.

THERE'S MILLIONS HERE FOR THE PICKIN'!

LOOKIT THAT! REAL STONES, MAN!

C'MON, SAL, LET'S GO, HUH? THIS PLACE SPOOKS ME.

YOU DON'T KNOW WHAT YOU'RE GONNA FIND...

STOP GRIPIN', YA DILD! LEND A HAND!

YOU **KILLED** THEM?

I GAVVE THEM **PEACCCE**...RESSSPITE FROM THEIR WICKEDNESSSS.

I–I THOUGHT YOU SAID YOU WOULDN'T HURT A FLY?

THEY WEREN'T FLIESSSS.

I SEE. SO...YOU HID THERE AMONG THE CORPSES. MUST'VE BEEN, UH...PRETTY DISGUSTING, ALL DECOMPOSING LIKE THAT..?

ON THE CONTRARY, IT WASSS MOSSST COMFORTABLE.

ASSSLEEP WITH THE PURE AND THE PURGGGGED...FOR MONTHSSS IT WASSS MY REFUGGGE, A SSSAFE COMFORTING COCOON...

...HIDDEN FROM THE PRYING EYESSS OF THE MEGA-CITY, THE PROBING TENDRILSSS OF CURSSSSED **PSSSI-DIVISION**—

"—FOR **WHICHHH** OF THEM WOULD READILY ALLOW THEIR MINDSSS TO DELVE AMONG SSUCHHH DIVINE SSSSLAUGHTER?"

BUT PERHAPS BESSST THAT I DID WAKE THENNN, FOR I HAD LINGERED LONGGG ENOUGH.

"I HAD MUCHHH TO DO— A MISSSION THAT WILL NEVER END."

Ic Mr Keever
Box room, suit small adult

24K MRS DOOBLE
Lge B-hab. Two Sharing

91A GOLDFRAB Bedshare, Day ONLY.

91F Ms. Quint
2 single B-habs. No pimps

133b Mrs Gunderson
Own room, lge lux-apt.
Suit business gent.
Privacy guaranteed.

" I NEEDED A BASSSE . . ."

HE WASSS UNHAPPY ABOUT MY PRESSSENCCCE HERE. I GRANTED HIM MERCCCCY.

B-BUT YOU SAID YOU WERE SICK OF KILLING!

SICK OF KILLINGGG AND NOT BEINGGG APRECCCCI-ATED FOR IT!

YEAH, WELL —ULP!—I'M NOT REALLY HONESTLY ALL THAT SURE I C-CAN CONTINUE THIS INTERVIEW.

I mean, I-I'm committing a serious crime if I even fail to tell the judges what I..I've seen.

Not that I'd want to, of course, but you-you know how it is...

SSSSIT DOWN, MR SSSSKUTER!

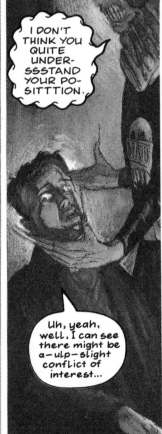

I DON'T THINK YOU QUITE UNDER-SSSTAND YOUR PO-SITTTION.

Uh, yeah, well, I can see there might be a—ulp—slight conflict of interest...

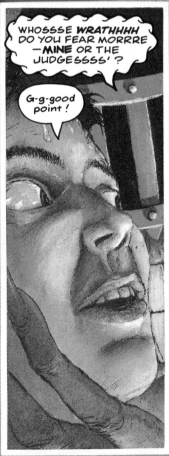

WHOSSSE WRATHHHH DO YOU FEAR MORRRE —MINE OR THE JUDGESSSS'?

G-g-good point!

RAP RAP!

RAISED VOICES, MR De'ATH? I DO HOPE THERE'S NO TROUBLE?

JUSSST A MINOR ALTERCATTION, MRSSS GUNDERSSSSON. BUT I THHHINK MR SSSKUTER ISS COMINGG ROUND TO MY WAY OF THHHINKINGGG. ISSS THAT NOT SSSO?

uh...

I CAMME TO THIS CCCITY ON AN ACT OF *MERCCCY,* MR SSSKUTER. TO BRINGGG JUSSSTICCCE TO THE GUILTY —DEATHHH TO THHE LIVVING... RELIEFFF FROM THE BURDEN OF THEIR MISSSERABLE LIVVESSS...

...FOR ALL *CRIME* ISSS COMITTTED BY THE *LIVVING* — THEREFORE ALL *LIFFFE* MUSSST BE A *CRIME.*

I—I DON'T THINK IT NECESSARILY FOLLOWS...

SSSSILENCCCE! YOU UNDERSSSSTAND NOTHHHINGGG!

YOU ARE LIKE THE RESSST OF THEM! UNGRATEFFUL RABBLE! TIME AND AGAIN THEY HAVVE SSSPURNED MY GENEROSSSITY, TURNED AWAY MY HELPINGG HAND! WELL, *NO MORE!*

I INTEND TO *LEAVE* THISS CITY, MR SSSKUTER, TO TAKE MYSSELF WHERE MY TALENTSSS WILL BE MORE...APPRECCCIATED.

BUT BEFFFORE I GO THE PEOPLE MUSSST BE GIVEN ONE LASSST CHANCCE TO REALISSSE THE FOLLY OF THEIR WAYSSSS...TO UNDERSSSSTAND WHY THEY MUSSST COME TO *LOVVE* DEATHHHH, ASSS I DO.

TO DO THAT THEY MUSSST KNOW *ME* — MUSSST *KNOW* WHAT HASS *MADE* ME WHAT I AM.

THE *WORLD* SSSHOULD KNOWWW MY SSSTORY, MR SSSKUTER. *YOU* WILL TELLL IT.

AN "ORIGINS". OH WOW.

ULP!

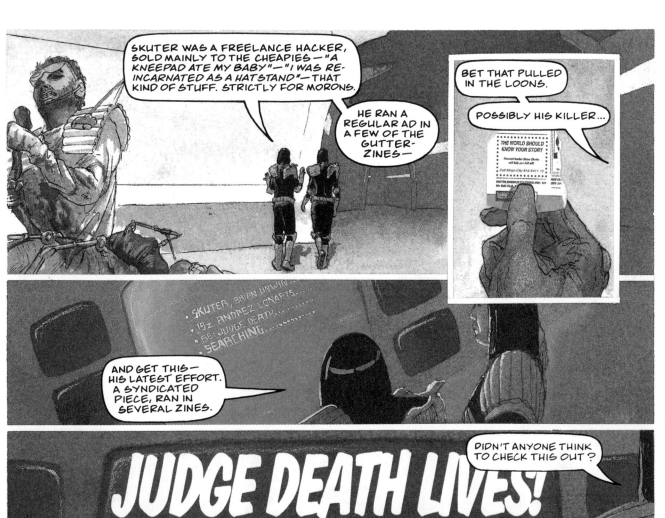

SKUTER WAS A FREELANCE HACKER, SOLD MAINLY TO THE CHEAPIES — "A KNEEPAD ATE MY BABY" — "I WAS RE-INCARNATED AS A HATSTAND" — THAT KIND OF STUFF. STRICTLY FOR MORONS.

HE RAN A REGULAR AD IN A FEW OF THE GUTTER-ZINES —

BET THAT PULLED IN THE LOONS.

POSSIBLY HIS KILLER...

• SKUTER, BRIAN DARWIN...
• 19z, ANDREZ CONAPTS...
• RE: JUDGE DEATH...
SEARCHING...

AND GET THIS — HIS LATEST EFFORT. A SYNDICATED PIECE, RAN IN SEVERAL ZINES.

JUDGE DEATH LIVES!

IS JUDGE DEATH YOUR NEXT DOOR NEIGHBOUR? By Our Man On Death's Doorstep!

Judge Death is alive and well and living in a city apartment.

I can reveal this startling news, writes Brian Skuter, because I came face to face with the doyen of darkness - and lived!

Though I am not at liberty to divulge his exact whereabouts, I can reveal that Death, listed as missing since his shock defeat in Necropolis, is very much a sadder and wiser...

In a frank interview... some foursome - also revealed to me...

* his re...

DIDN'T ANYONE THINK TO CHECK THIS OUT?

THEY MUST'VE FIGURED IT FOR THE USUAL HOKUM.

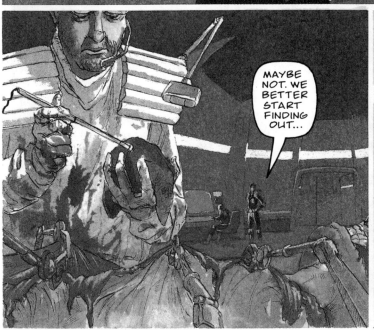

MAYBE NOT. WE BETTER START FINDING OUT...

I'LL CHECK HIS APARTMENT. CALL IN PSI-DIVISION, SEE WHAT THEY MAKE OF IT. AND INFORM DREDD —

IF DEATH IS BACK IN TOWN, HE'LL WANT TO KNOW.

AS THE DARK JUDGE TALKED I FOUND IT DIFFICULT TO QUELL THE GROWING SUSPICION THAT THIS WAS ALL A DREAM—THAT I WOULD WAKE AND FIND MYSELF SAFE AND WELL, BACK IN MY OLD FAMILIAR APARTMENT AGAIN...

COULD I REALLY BE CALMLY SITTING THERE, LISTENING TO THE MOST EVIL BEING IN HISTORY RECOUNTING TALES OF HIS BOYHOOD...

SO... YOU KILLED YOUR DOG. WAS WOOFIE YOUR FIRST KILLING?

ON ANY SSSERIOUSSS LEVEL, YESSS. I'D TORTURED MY SSSHARE OF SSSMALL ANIMALSS AND INSSSECTSSS, OF COURSSSE...

I GOT MY OWN BACK ON SSSISSS ASS WELL...

AHHHHHHHHHHH

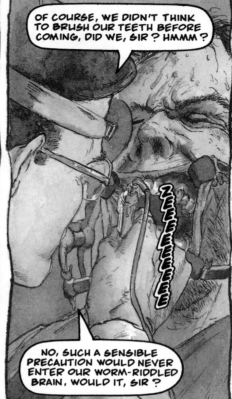

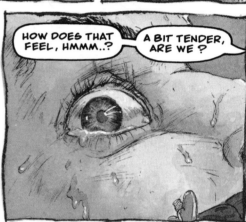

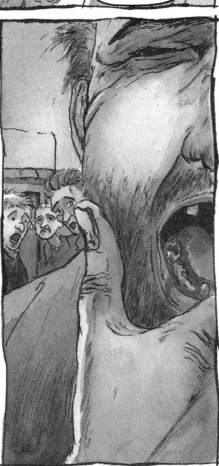

SURELY YOU AND YOUR FATHER COULDN'T GET AWAY WITH TREATING PATIENTS LIKE THAT FOR LONG?

ON THE CONTRARY.

PEOPLE SSSUFFFER FROM A DEEEP-ROOTED DREAD OF DENTISSTSSS, ASSS OF SSSERPENTSSS AND CREEPINGG THINGGSSS. NONE WERE IN A FFIT SSTATE TO COMPLAIN WHEN THEY LEFFT—FEWW COMPLAINED AFTERWARDSSS.

PERHAPSSS THEY FFEARED THAT IFF THEY MADE A FUSSS THEN SSSOMEHOW MY FFFATHHER WOULD COME FFOR THEM AGAIN...

YOU HAVE NICCE WHITE TEEETHHH, MR SSSKUTER. I COULD SSTILL DO A NICCCE JJJOB ON YOU.

I-IF YOU DON'T MIND I'LL, UH, PASS ON THAT ONE... GOLDEN OPPORTUNITY, I KNOW...

IN THE END, ASSS ISSS THE NATURE OF THINGGSSS, MERE TORTURE DID NOT SSSUFFFICCE. MY FFATHHHER TOOK TO DESSSPATCHHINGG HISSS PATIENTSS WHENEVER POSSSIBLE...

...HE WHO SSSHOWED ME THE INHERENT CORRUPTION OF LIFFFE...AND THE TRUE FORGIVVINGGG NATURE OF DEATHHHH...

HEAVE HO, SIDNEY!

I SSHHALL ALWAYSSS BE GRATEFFUL TO HIM. ASSS I SSSAY, MY PHHILOSSSOPHHY OF LIFFE AND DEATHHH WASS DEVELOPINGGG. IT WASSS HE WHO HELPED ME PUT IT INTO WORDSSS...

THANK YOU, MADAM, DON'T CALL AGAIN.

IF THOSE TEETH GIVE YOU ANY MORE TROUBLE YOU JUST LET ME KNOW, SIR.

PEOPLE! THEIR BRAINS ARE FULL OF WORMS. DID YOU KNOW THAT, SIDNEY?

NO, DAD.

LITTLE WRIGGLING WORMS— BRAINS LIKE RIPE, WRITHING PUSTULES, JUST WAITING TO BURST, TO SPEW THEIR FOULNESS OVER US.

EVEN MUM AND SIS?

ALL OF THEM. WORMS.

THEY'RE BETTER OFF DEAD. THEY'RE AT PEACE NOW.

WE'VE DONE THEM A FAVOUR. WE'VE KILLED THE WORMS.

ONLY THE *DEAD* ARE TRULY WITHOUT WORMS. REMEMBER THAT, SIDNEY.

YES, DAD.

WORMS?

I DID NOT TAKE HIM LITERALLLY. MY FFATHHHER WASS OBVIOUSSSLY SSSOME-WHAT FFANCIFFFUL.

BUT I UNDERSSSTOOOD HIM WELLL ENOUGHHH. I SSSAW IT ASS A METAPHHOR FFFOR *SSSINFFFULNESSS*...

ONLY THE DEAD ARE TRULY WITHHOUT SSSIN. IT ISSS A TRUTHHH EVEN YOU CANNOT DENY, MR SSSKUTER.

WELL, NO, I GUESS NOT. WE ALL DO BAD THINGS...

LIFFE IS, BY ITSSS VERY NATURE, SSSINFFFULLL. ONLY DEATHHH CAN RELIEVE ITS BURDEN. ONLY IN DEATHHH CAN MAN'SSS TROUBLED SSSOUL FIND PEACCCCE.

TORTURING PATIENTSSS WASS ONE THINGG, SSSYSSSTEMATIC SSUSSSTAINED HOMICCIDE BY DENTISSSTRY QUITE ANOTHHER — FOR IN THOSSSE BENIGHTED TIMESSS SSUCHHH ACTSSS OF MERCCY WERE SSSTILL CLASS-SSIFFIED ASS CRIMESSS.

MY FFATHHHER'SSS ACTIVVITIESSS COULD NOT FOREVVER REMAIN A SSSECRET.

I MADE SSSURE OF IT BY REPORTINGGG HIM MYSSSELFF.

YOU STOOLED ON YOUR OWN DAD?

INDEED. I HAD BEEN GIVVINGGG SSSOME THOUGHT TO MY FFFUTURE. DENTISSSTRY HAD A CCERTAIN APPEAL, BUT PROSSS-PECTSSS WERE LIMITED. I REQUIRED A CAREER WHERE I WOULD HAVE AMPLE SSSCOPE TO APPLY MY IDEASSSS...

FORENSIC

MOBILE

GOOD WORK, SON.

THANK YOU, SIR.

JOIN THE JUDGES

* Beat people up
* Kill anyone you like (within reason)
* Good rates of pay
* Plenty of graft
* Vicious nature a plus
* LUNCHEON VOUCHERS

INTERESTED?

YES, SIR.

GOOD! WE CAN USE A BRIGHT YOUNG LAD LIKE YOU!

SO... YOU EXECUTED YOUR OWN FATHER.

YESSS. A CHERISSHHED MEMOREE.

I WASSS AN IMMEDIATE SSUCCESSS AT LAW SSSCHOOL, ASS WE CALLED IT. MY GRASSSP OF MATTERSS PHHILOSSSOPHICAL WAS GROWINGGG FASST. I WASSS ABLE TO ENGAGE MY TUTORSS IN LONGG DISSCUSSIONSS, IMPRESSSINGG MANY WITHH THE SSIMPLE LOGIC OF MY ARGUMENT.

A FEWW, HOWEVVER, THOUGHT ME SSSICK.

YOU DON'T SAY.

THEY WERE LIKE YOU, MR SSSKUTER-MINDSS LOCKED IN THE PASST, IN THE OLD THINKINGGG. THE "WETSSS", I CALLED THEM.

THEY REGARDED ME ASS AN EXXCRESSCENCCE WHICHHH MUSSST BE REMOVVED.

THEYY UNDERESSSTIMATED THEIR ENEMY!

HOWW WELL I REMEMBER THE DEPUTY PRINCIPAL'SSS TRAGIC SSSUICCIDE IN THE FIFFTH YEAR TORTURE LAB...

GOODBY CRULE WURLD

SUPERRACK 91 [FULLY OPEN]

" ... AND THE FFIRE IN THE SSENIOR TUTORSSS' QUARTERSSS WHICHH CLAIMED FFOUR LIVESSS.

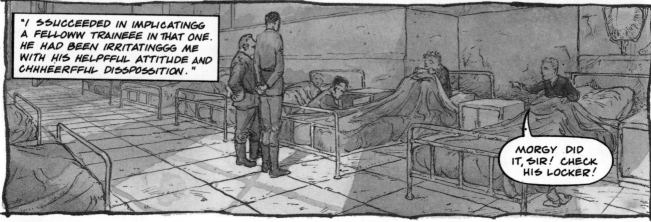

"I SSUCCEEDED IN IMPLICATINGG A FELLOWW TRAINEEE IN THAT ONE. HE HAD BEEN IRRITATINGGG ME WITH HIS HELPFFUL ATTITUDE AND CHHEERFFUL DISSPOSSITION."

MORGY DID IT, SIR! CHECK HIS LOCKER!

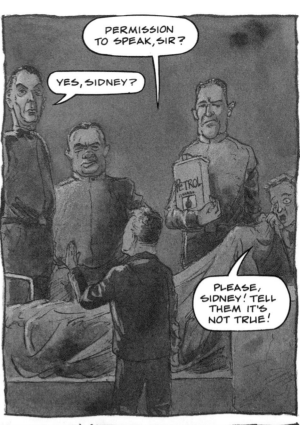

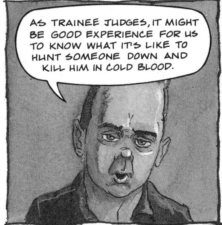

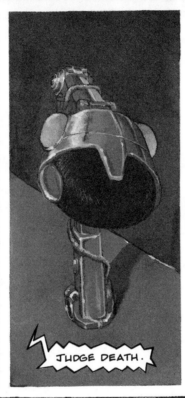

THE *HIGH* POINT OF MY LAWW SSSCHOOL DAYSSS — MY CROWNINGGG MOMENT — CAME IN MY SIXTHHH YEAR...

IT WASS THE CUSSSTOM TO ALLOW EACHH TRAINEE JJUDGGE THEIR *DAY* IN *COURT* — PRESSIDING OVER PETTY OFFFENCCES AND CIVVIL MATTERSSS, FOR THE MOSST PART.

NO ONE WHO WITNESSSED *MY* DAY IN COURT WOULD EVER FORGET IT...

ALL RISE FOR TRAINEE JUDGE SIDNEY!

FIRST CASE!

BAM!

THE DEFENDANT IS CHARGED WITH *LOITERING* IN A NO-LOITER ZONE.

HOW DO YOU PLEAD?

GUILTY, YOUR HONOUR.

"MY FINAL CASSSE, I REMEMBER, WASS A *DIVVORCCCE*..."

YOUR HONOUR, OUR CLIENTS HAVE EXPERIENCED A SUDDEN DESIRE TO *SETTLE* THEIR DIFFERENCES AND NO LONGER WISH TO PROCEED WITH THE ACTION!

AND THIS IS THE DECISION OF YOU BOTH?

Y-YES, YOUR HONOUR!

YOU—YOU GOTTA BELIEVE US! WE LOVE EACH OTHER VERY MUCH!

I'M GLAD TO HEAR THAT. AND MAY I SAY IT DOES THIS COURT GOOD TO BE ABLE TO BRING TWO PEOPLE BACK TOGETHER AGAIN FOR A CHANGE. MY GOOD WISHES FOR A LONG AND HAPPY LIFE TOGETHER.

THANK MERCY!

BDAM!

THUNK!

THUNK!

WASTING COURT TIME. SENTENCE IS *DEATH.*

MY DAYY IN COURT CAUSSED A FFLOOD OF COMPLAINTSSS.

I CAN IMAGINE.

"THE PRINCCIPAL CALLED ME IN THE NEXXT DAYY. HE FELT MY ACTIONSSS HAD BEEN EXXCESSSIVVE..."

ONE OF THEM, SIDNEY—TWO OR THREE, MAYBE! YOU WERE GUNNING DOWN EVERYONE!

AS PRESIDING JUDGE THAT WAS MY RIGHT, SIR.

I KNOW, SIDNEY, BUT DIVORCEES—?

THAT WAS A JUDGEMENT CALL, SIR.

BUT THEY WERE INNOCENT, SIDNEY!

NOBODY'S INNOCENT, SIR. ONLY THE DEAD.

I BELIEVE MY SENTENCING WAS ENTIRELY APPROPRIATE. IF YOU CHECK OUR OWN STATISTICS YOU'LL SEE THAT 87 PER CENT OF CONVICTED PERPETRATORS WILL COMMIT ANOTHER OFFENCE —AND THESE ARE JUST THE ONES WE KNOW ABOUT.

HOW MANY OF THE PEOPLE I SENTENCED WILL RE-OFFEND?

WHY, NONE, BUT—

EXACTLY! EVEN YOU HAVE GOT TO ADMIT THOSE ARE GOOD FIGURES, SIR.

THEY ARE TOTALLY REHABILITATED. NOT ONE OF THEM WILL EVER COMMIT ANOTHER CRIME. AS FAR AS THEY ARE CONCERNED, I HAVE CURED THE CRIME PROBLEM.

YES, I SEE THAT, BUT—

NO, YOU DON'T SEE, SIR! WE'RE NOT JUST TALKING ABOUT A HANDFUL OF PEOPLE IN A MINOR COURT. THERE'S A BROADER ISSUE AT STAKE.

THINK OF IT, SIR! FOR CENTURIES WE'VE BEEN SEARCHING FOR THE *CURE* FOR *CRIME* — AND I HAVE FOUND IT! *I HAVE SHOWN THE WAY!*

AH, SIDNEY, YOU'LL BE THE DEATH OF US ALL.

YES, SIR.

"AFFTER THAT I WASSS THE TALK OF LAWW SSCHOOL. SSOME OF THE OTTHER TRAINEEES BEGAN TO REFFER TO ME ASS SSSIDNEYY *DEATHHH.*"

"I WASSS MOSST TAKEN BY THE NAME. I ADOPTED IT. I BECAME...*TRAINEEE JJUDGGE DEATHHH.*"

TRAINEE **DEATH** JUDGE

THEY MEANT IT ASS A CHHILDISSHHH *JIBE*, OF COURSSE — TO MOCK ME. BUT THE LAUGHTER OF FOOLSSS CANNOT WOUND THE WISSSE. I KNEW THAT TIME WOULD PROVVE ME RIGHT. I KNEW MY OWN WORTHHH.

HE IS A PROUD ALIEN FIEND — A TRIFLE VAIN, PERHAPS, BUT ASSURED IN THE KNOWLEDGE OF HIS OWN RECTITUDE, PROUD OF HIS ACHIEVEMENTS.

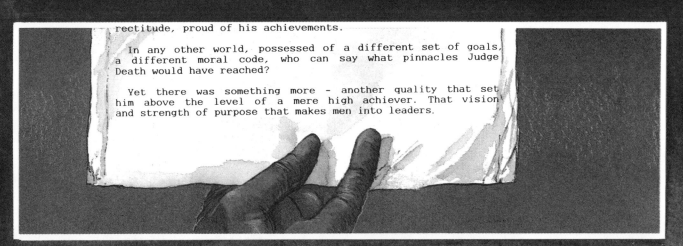

rectitude, proud of his achievements.

In any other world, possessed of a different set of goals, a different moral code, who can say what pinnacles Judge Death would have reached?

Yet there was something more - another quality that set him above the level of a mere high achiever. That vision and strength of purpose that makes men into leaders.

I GRADUATED FROM LAWW SSCHOOL WITHH FULL HONOURSSS. I NOW HAD A LICENCCCE TO KILLL.

IF THAT'S NOT THE REAL McCOY IT'S A PRETTY GOOD IMITATION!

YOU SAY SKUTER GOT ANOTHER CALL FROM THIS GEEK?

HE SOUNDED REAL ANGRY- TOLD BRI HE BETTER GET OVER THERE PRONTO OR ALLL WOULD GO ILLL WITHHH HIM — KNOW WHAT I MEAN? CREEE-PO!

I GOT THE ADDRESS IF YOU WANT IT.

CONTROL, I'M BEGINNING TO THINK SKUTER'S KILLER COULD BE JUDGE DEATH. BETTER CALL IN ANDERSON, JUST IN CASE.

GET UNITS TO APARTMENT 133b, SYLVIA PLATH BLOCK.

APARTMENT REGISTERED IN THE NAME GUNDERSON.

INTERVIEW LODGER— A MR JAY De'ATH...

I WASSS NOT ALONE. THERE WERE MANY WHO FFOLLOWED MY LEAD, WHO SSSAW THE TRUTHH OF MY MESSSAGE, WHO RECOGNISSED IN ME THE HAND OF *DESSSTINY* AT WORK.

"THERE WERE *THHREE* IN PARTICULAR— YOUNGGG JJUDGESSS WHO HAD GRADUATED BELOWW ME. THEY HAD BEEN MY ADMIRERSSS IN LAWW SSSCHOOL—THEY BECAME MY MOSSST TRUSSTED LIEUTENANTSSS."

"AHHH, WHAT *HEADY* DAYSSS THEY WERE! WHAT *TIMESSS* WE HAD, JUDGINGGG THE PEOPLE TO OUR YOUNG HEARTSSS CONTENT.'"

"IT WASSS SSTILL NECESSSARY TO OFFER SSOME PALTRY JUSSSTIFFICATION FOR OUR ACTIVITIESSS— *LIFFFE* ITSSELFF HAD NOT YET BEEN DECLARED ILLEGAL."

"BUT A CRIME COULD ALWAYSSS BE FOUND. THAT ISS THE NATURE OF LIFFFE. ALLL ARE GUILTY."

"HOW WELL I REMEMBER THE DAY ONE OF MY YOUNG BUCKSSS SSSENTENCCCED AN ENTIRE SSSCHOOL TO DEATHHH— BREACHHH OF *NOISSSE* REGSSS AT PLAYTIME! OVER EIGHTEEN HUNDRED YOUNGGG SSSINNERSS ROASSSTED TO A CRISSSP."

"IT WASS RATHER A LARGE COMPREHHENSSSIVE, I RECALL..."

FFOR YEARSSS A SSECTION OF THE TOWN HAD HAD A FFEARFFUL REPUTATION. PEOPLE DISSAPPEARED AND WERE NEVER SSEEN AGAIN. THERE WERE RUMOURSSS OF **DEMONSSS** WHICH DWELT IN CAVVE SYSTEMSSS DEEP BELOW GROUND...

"I DECCIDED TO INVESSSTIGATE..."

"WHAT I FFOUND WASSS BEYOND MY WILDESSST EXXPECTATIONSSS—"

A JUDGE, SISSTER...

I THINK HE'S COME TO KILL US...

YESSS.

HEEHEE HEE HEE HEE HEE HEE HEE HEE HEE

"PHHOBIA AND NAUSSSEA WERE THEIR NAMESS. THEY WERE DEATHHH CULTISSTSSS AND DEVOTEESS OF THE DARK ARTSSS. THEY DERIVED THEIR POWER FFROM HUMAN SSACRIFFICCCE..."

"IT WASSS LOVVVE AT FFIRSSST SSSIGHT!"

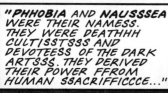

YOU SEEM SUCH PRECIOUS CREATURES...

IT WOULD BE A SHAME TO HURT YOU... JUST YET.

WHO CAN EXXPLAIN LOVVVE? IT SSTRIKESSS WHEN WE LEASSST EXXPECT!

ALLL I KNOW ISSS, ASS I BEHELD THEM THERE, A PICTURE OF DEMENTED LOVELINESSS—

—ASS I GAZZZED UPON THE DIVINE MADNESSSS IN THEIR EYESSS—

—I FELT A SSSTIRRINGG IN MY BREASST AND IN MY LOINSSS SSUCHH ASS I HAD NEVER FFELT BEFFORE...

FFROM THAT MOMENT I WASSS THEIRSSSS!

SO IT WAS THE *SISTERS* OF *DEATH* WHO TURNED YOU INTO A ZOMBIE.

I DO NOT LIKE THAT TERM, MR SSSKUTER.

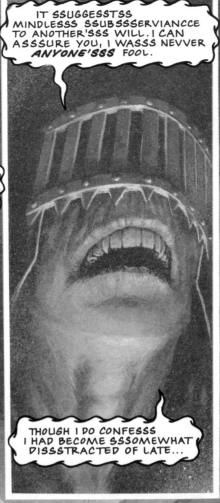

IT SSUGGESSTSS MINDLESSS SSUBSSSERVIANCCE TO ANOTHER'SSS WILL. I CAN ASSSURE YOU, I WASSS NEVVER *ANYONE'SSS* FOOL.

THOUGH I DO CONFESSS I HAD BECOME SSSOMEWHAT DISSSTRACTED OF LATE...

IT CAN HAPPEN TO THE MOSSST FAR-SSSIGHTED OF USS — WE BECOME BOGGED DOWN IN THE PRACTICAL, DAY-TO-DAY ASSSPECTSSS, LOSSSE SSIGHT OF THE BROADER PERSSSPECTIVVE...

ONCE AGAIN THAT NOTE OF MISSIONARY ZEAL IN HIS VOICE... TO WRITE JUDGE DEATH OFF AS A MERE ALIEN FIEND WOULD BE UNWISE. HERE WAS THE VISIONARY, THE PROPHET, THE MAN WITH A MISSION AND A MESSAGE FOR HIS PEOPLE.

93 ↑

DARE I SAY IT — IN HIS OWN TWISTED TERMS, A MESSIAH...

NOW I WASSS FILLED WITHH NEWW ENERGGY. I COULD SSEE SSUDDENLY THAT DESSSTINY WASS WITHHIN MY GRASSSP—FFOR WHO COULD SSSTAND AGAINSST ME NOW?

WITHH MY FAITHHHFFUL LIEUTENANTSSS I PAID A CALL ON OUR *CHHIEFFF JJUDGGE*...

AHH, *DEATH,* YES... I'VE BEEN MEANING TO HAVE A WORD WITH YOU.

IT'S ALL THIS KILLING... KILLING, KILLING, KILLING!

THE PEOPLE ARE GUILTYY. THEY MUSSST BE JJUDGGGED.

YES, YES, GRANTED, BUT CAN'T YOU OCCASIONALLY JUST *ARREST* SOMEONE?

THAT'S A TERRIBLE *HISS* YOU'RE DEVELOPING, BY THE WAY.

CORPSES, CORPSES, EVERYWHERE YOU GO—YOU AND THOSE BULLY BOYS OF YOURS! AND IT'S NOT JUST YOU—*EVERY-BODY'S* AT IT NOW!

I JUST DON'T KNOW WHAT TO DO WITH YOU, DEATH. YOU ACT LIKE YOU WON'T BE SATISFIED TILL THE WHOLE *WORLD'S* DEAD!

YESSS, SSSIR!

THE *CRIME* ISSS *LIFFFE,* SSSSIR—

THE *SSSENTENCCE* ISSSS *DEATHHH!*

"THAT MAY SSEEM HARSHHH, BUT BELIEVVE ME, IT WASSS NECCESSSARY."

GET BACK IN YOUR APARTMENT. LOCK THE DOOR.

133k

"COMPARE OUR SSSTATISSTICSSS—"

ON *DEADWORLD* THERE ISSS NO ROBBERY—NO MURDER—NO ARSSSON—NO LITTERINGGG—NO NOISSY PARTIESSS TO DISSTURB THE NEIGHBOURSSS.

NO NEIGHBOURSSS.

NO EVVIL LURKINGGG IN THE HEARTSSS OF MEN. NO *CRIME*, MR SSSKUTER.

YOU CANNOT ARGUE WITHHH SSSTATISSTICSSS. *DEATHHH* ISS THE SSSOLUTION. *DEATHHHH CURESSS ALLL.*

THHANK YOU FFOR COMINGGG, MR SSSKUTER.

YOU MEAN—THAT'S IT? I... I CAN GO NOW?

YOU CAN GO NOWW.

LET THE PEOPLE KNOW MY SSSTORY. I WANT THEM TO UNDERSSTAND ...THERE *ISS* AN ALTERNATIVVE.

THEY HAVVE REJJECTED ME THISSS TIME, BUT SSSOME DAY THEY WILL COME TO RECOGNISSSE THE TRUE *WICKEDNESSS* OF THEIR LIVESSS.

TELL THEM...WHEN THEY DO—WHEN THEY ARE *READY* TO RECCEIVVE *MERCCY*— *I WILL RETURN.*

UH... RIGHT.

HIS BALEFUL GAZE NEVER LEFT ME AS I HASTILY PACKED. I COULDN'T ESCAPE THE TERRIBLE SUSPICION THAT HE WAS TOYING WITH ME, THAT I WOULD NEVER BE ALLOWED TO LEAVE THIS HOUSE...

MR SSSKUTER—

MY *BROTHERSSS*...
THE PLACE WHERE THEY ARE BEINGG HELD—ANY CHANCCCE OF... *SSSPRINGGINGGG* THEM?

I...I DON'T THINK SO. IT'S TRIPLE SECURITY. THEY'VE GOT SUCTION TRAPS AND A TEAM OF PSI JUDGES ON PERMANENT DUTY, JUST IN CASE YOU SHOW.

I THHOUGHT ASS MUCHH. THANK YOU.

OH...MR SSSKUTER—

ONE FFINAL THHINGGG...

Y...YES..?

I'M A LITTLE *SSSHORT* AT THE MOMENT. I WONDER IF YOU COULD PERHAPSSS SSEE YOUR WAY...

JUSSST ENOUGH TO COVVER THE RENT.

UH, YEAH. I GUESS...

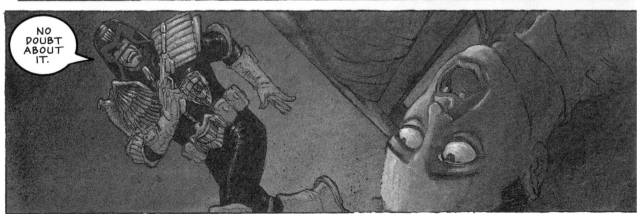

RAISED VOICES AGAIN, MR De'ATH?

GOODNESS ME, YOU BOYS DO GET YOURSELVES HET UP ABOUT THINGS, DON'T YOU?

MY APOLOGGIESSS, MRS GUNDERSSSON. IT WON'T HAPPEN AGAIN. MR SSSKUTER WILL BE LEAVINGGG SSHHORTLY.

HE ISS ABOUT TO BE TAKEN *UNWELLL.*

Oh jeez, please...

GOOD. FINE. SORRY TO HEAR THAT.

DO CARRY ON, BOYS.

LOOK, IT W-WASN'T MY FAULT! HONEST! I-I DID YOU A REALLY NICE PIECE— A PROPER IN-DEPTH PROFILE— B-BUT THEY WOULDN'T BUY IT!

THEY THOUGHT I WAS MAKING IT UP! THEY WOULDN'T BELIEVE YOU WERE HERE, IN THE CITY— TH-THEY FIGURED PSI-DIVISION WOULD HAVE KNOWN ABOUT IT—

Oh jeez...

THEY WOULDN'T BELIEVVVE YOU—!

WE'LL GIVVVE THEM SSSOMTHHINGGG TO BELIEVVVE IN, SSHHALL WE?

THE END